Our Family Story

Record your very own
unique family story

Call it a clan, call it a network,
call it a tribe, call it a family.
Whatever you call it, whoever you are,
you need one.

Jane Howard

Alicat

140 Albert Road
South Melbourne VIC 3205
Australia
Email: publishing@alicat.com.au

Copyright © Alicat Trading Pty Ltd, 2011
Images used under license from Shutterstock.com
and Thinkstock.com

Publisher: Ali Horgan
Project Manager: Angie McKenzie
Design: Canary Graphic Design

Contents

The family is one of
nature's masterpieces.

George Santayan

Our Family Story

Every story starts somewhere. Now you can record your family's story for all the family to see and enjoy. Create your own family's cherished heirloom of memories and facts about yourself and your ancestors. Here, in *Our Family Story*, you can record all of those family facts and quirks that perhaps only you have been told.

In this book, we have allowed space for you to record back as far as your great grandparents. If you are one of the lucky ones that can delve even further back into your family history, there is a pocket at the back of the book to hold that information.

If you only know scant information about your parents, grandparents and great grandparents, use this book as a launching pad to discover your family tree with the help of other family members and friends. They may have a story they remember or a piece of information that can help you recreate your family's past. Bring your forebearers back to life with intimate information about them and record it here in the one place.

As we move into the twenty-first century, communication is mostly electronic and instant. We look up details and facts on the internet rather than record them on paper. Our children don't think to ask about past family members – to them, everything is about now and the future. How will they ever know about the generations who created them?

This journal will stop the loss of precious information and, starting with you, create a lasting record of your family – past and present. Include not only the facts, but the information you want them to know and remember about you and your relatives.

Not often do you get the chance to lay down a foundation for your family to reflect on and add to. By filling in this journal you will do just that! Your family story will be recorded for all to see and enjoy.

So go ahead, introduce your future to your past!

My Family Tree

_____ _____
My mother's father   My father's father

_____ _____
My mother's mother   My father's mother

_____ _____
My mother   My father

_____
Me

_____

_____

_____

_____

My children

My Partner's Family Tree

_____   _____
My partner's mother's father   My partner's father's father

_____   _____
My partner's mother's mother   My partner's father's mother

_____   _____
My partner's mother   My partner's father

_____
My partner

_____

_____

_____

_____
Our children

All About Me

My full name *(as on your birth certificate)*
_____

_____

I liked to be called _____

I was named after _____

I was known by the family as _____

Date of birth _____ Time of birth _____

Birthplace _____

_____

Height _____ My eye colour _____

_____

They say I take after _____

_____

My religion _____

I lived with *(parents, siblings, others)* _____

_____

_____

I was the *(first, second, etc.)* _____ child in a family of _____ children

My siblings *(name and date of birth)* _____

_____

_____

_____

Major events and upheavals in my life _____

_____

_____

_____

ATTACH A FAVOURITE PHOTOGRAPH
OF YOURSELF HERE

A family is a unit composed not only
of children but of men,
women, an occasional animal,
and the common cold.

Ogden Nash

My Parents and Grandparents

My mother's given name _____

She liked to be called _____

Her full maiden name *(as on her birth certificate)* _____

_____

My mother's mother's full name _____

Her full maiden name *(as on her birth certificate)* _____

_____

My mother's father's full name *(as on his birth certificate)* _____

_____

My mother's siblings and dates of birth _____

_____

_____

My father's given name *(as on his birth certificate)* _____

_____

He liked to be called _____

My father's mother's full name _____

Her full maiden name *(as on her birth certificate)* _____

_____

My father's father's full name *(as on his birth certificate)* _____

_____

My father's siblings and dates of birth _____

_____

_____

There are two lasting
bequests we can give
our children.
One is roots.
The other is wings.

Hodding Carter, Jr

My Great Grandparents

***

MY MOTHER'S GRANDPARENTS
(on the mother's side)

Great grandmother's maiden name
_____

_____

Great grandfather's name
_____

_____

MY MOTHER'S GRANDPARENTS
(on the father's side)

Great grandmother's maiden name
_____

_____

Great grandfather's name
_____

_____

MY FATHER'S GRANDPARENTS
(on the mother's side)

Great grandmother's maiden name
_____

_____

Great grandfather's name
_____

_____

MY FATHER'S GRANDPARENTS
(on the father's side)

Great grandmother's maiden name
_____

_____

Great grandfather's name
_____

_____

My Partner

His/her full name (as on his/her birth certificate)

_____

_____

He/she liked to be called _____

He/she was named after _____

Known by the family as _____

Date of birth _____ Time of birth _____

Birthplace _____

Height _____ His/her eye colour _____

They say he/she takes after _____

His/her religion _____

He/she lived with (parents, siblings, others)

_____

He/she was the (first, second, etc.) _____ in a family of _____ children

His/her siblings (name and date of birth)

_____

_____

_____

Major events and upheavals in his/her life

_____

_____

_____

_____

_____

_____

_____

ATTACH A FAVOURITE PHOTOGRAPH
OF YOUR PARTNER AS A CHILD HERE

The advantage of growing up with siblings is that you become very good at fractions.

Robert Brault

My Partner's Parents and Grandparents

My partner's mother's name

_____

She liked to be called

_____

Her full maiden name (as on her birth certificate)

_____

_____

My partner's mother's mother's full name

_____

Her full maiden name (as on her birth certificate)

_____

_____

My partner's mother's father's full name (as on his birth certificate)

_____

_____

He liked to be called

_____

My partner's mother's siblings and dates of birth

_____

_____

My partner's father's given name (as on his birth certificate)

_____

_____

He liked to be called

_____

My partner's father's mother's full name

_____

Her full maiden name (as on her birth certificate)

_____

_____

My partner's father's father's full name (as on his birth certificate)

_____

_____

He liked to be called

_____

My partner's father's siblings and dates of birth

_____

_____

_____

> It is not flesh and blood but the heart which makes us fathers and sons.
>
> _Johann Schiller_

My Partner's
Great Grandparents

HIS/HER MOTHER'S GRANDPARENTS
(on the mother's side)

Great grandmother's maiden name

_____

Great grandfather's name

_____

HIS/HER MOTHER'S GRANDPARENTS
(on the father's side)

Great grandmother's maiden name

_____

Great grandfather's name

_____

HIS/HER FATHER'S GRANDPARENTS
(on the mother's side)

Great grandmother's maiden name

_____

Great grandfather's name

_____

HIS/HER FATHER'S GRANDPARENTS
(on the father's side)

Great grandmother's maiden name

_____

Great grandfather's name

_____

My Mother

Given name

Maiden name

Nickname

We called her

Date of birth   Time of birth

Birthplace

Height   Eye colour

Colouring

Nationality

She was the *(first, second, etc.)*   in a family of   children

Her siblings

She grew up in *(place)*

Her schools

Her age when she left school

Further education and training

Degrees and diplomas

Her occupation

Organisations she worked for

ATTACH A FAVOURITE PHOTOGRAPH
OF YOUR MOTHER HERE

Special interests and talents _____

_____

_____

Her best friends _____

_____

_____

Special memories of my mother _____

_____

_____

_____

_____

_____

_____

_____

_____

> All women become
> like their mothers.
> That is their
> tragedy.
> No man does.
> That's his.
>
> *Oscar Wilde*

My Father

Given name

Nickname

We called him

Date of birth   Time of birth

Birthplace

Height   Eye colour

Colouring

Nationality

He was the *(first, second, etc.)*   in a family of   children

His siblings

He grew up in *(place)*

His schools

His age when he left school

Further education and training

Degrees and diplomas

His occupation

Organisations he worked for

ATTACH A FAVOURITE PHOTOGRAPH
OF YOUR FATHER HERE

Special interests and talents

His best friends

Special memories of my father

It is much easier
to become
a father than to
be one.

Kent Nerburn

My Parent's Marriage

How they met _____

Date of marriage _____

Where it took place _____

The bride wore _____

The bridegroom wore _____

The reception was held at _____

Guests included _____

Where they spent their honeymoon _____

Where they lived on their return _____

Addresses of their later family homes _____

_____

_____

They were married for _____ years

Memories of their life together _____

_____

_____

_____

_____

_____

_____

_____

_____

_____

_____

_____

_____

ATTACH A FAVOURITE PHOTOGRAPH
OF YOUR PARENTS HERE

Happy marriages begin when
we marry the ones we love,
and they blossom when
we love the ones we marry.

Tom Mullen

My Partner's Mother

Given name

Maiden name

We called her

Date of birth   Time of birth

Birthplace

Height   Eye colour

Colouring

Nationality

She was the *(first, second, etc.)*   in a family of   children

Her siblings

She grew up in *(place)*

Her schools

Her age when she left school

Further education and training

Degrees and diplomas

Her occupation

Organisations she worked for

ATTACH A FAVOURITE PHOTOGRAPH OF
YOUR PARTNER'S MOTHER HERE

Special interests and talents

Her best friends

Special memories of your partner's mother

> A mother is a person
> who seeing there are
> only four pieces of
> pie for five people,
> promptly announces
> she never did care
> for pie.
>
> *Tenneva Jordan*

My Partner's Father

Given name

Nickname

We called him

Date of birth   Time of birth

Birthplace

Height   Eye colour

Colouring

Nationality

He was the *(first, second, etc.)*   in a family of   children

His siblings

He grew up in *(place)*

His schools

His age when he left school

Further education and training

Degrees and diplomas

His occupation

Organisations he worked for

ATTACH A FAVOURITE PHOTOGRAPH OF
YOUR PARTNER'S FATHER HERE

Special interests and talents
_____
_____
_____

His best friends
_____
_____

Special memories of his/her father
_____
_____
_____
_____
_____
_____
_____

Any man can be
a father. It takes
someone special
to be a dad.

Author Unknown

My Partner's Parents' Marriage

How they met _____

_____

Date of marriage _____

Where it took place _____

_____

The bride wore _____

_____

The bridegroom wore _____

The reception was held at _____

_____

Guests included _____

_____

_____

_____

_____

Where they spent their honeymoon _____

_____

Where they lived on their return _____

_____

Addresses of their later family homes _____

_____

_____

They were married for _____ years

ATTACH A FAVOURITE PHOTOGRAPH OF
YOUR PARTNER'S PARENTS HERE

Success in marriage does not
come merely through finding
the right mate,
but through being the right mate.

Barnett Brickner

My Childhood

Names of primary schools

_____

Favourite playground games

_____

Best friends in primary school

Pocket money   What I spent it on

_____

Household chores

_____

Names of secondary schools

_____

Favourite subjects

Favourite teachers

Best friends in secondary school

_____

Favourite books

_____

Favourite music

_____

Favourite television shows, movies and actors

_____

Favourite sports

_____

ATTACH A FAVOURITE PHOTOGRAPH
FROM YOUR CHILDHOOD HERE

Childhood holidays

Makes and models of family cars

Childhood pets

Special childhood memories

My Adult Years

Tertiary education
_____

_____

Degrees and diplomas
_____

_____

My first job was with *(name of organisation)*
_____

_____

My position
_____

Weekly salary _____ Price of a newspaper _____

Special friends
_____

_____

Favourite sporting teams
_____

_____

Favourite music
_____

_____

Favourite books
_____

_____

Favourite television shows
_____

_____

_____

Favourite movies and actors
_____

_____

_____

> Age is an issue of
> mind over matter.
> If you don't mind,
> it doesn't matter.
>
> *Mark Twain*

Other jobs *(names of organisations and positions held)*

_____
_____
_____
_____
_____

Special interests and pastimes

_____
_____
_____
_____

Special memories and achievements

_____
_____
_____
_____
_____
_____
_____
_____
_____

What I consider my strengths to be

_____
_____
_____
_____
_____
_____
_____

My Partner's Childhood

Names of primary schools _____

_____

Favourite playground games _____

_____

_____

Best friends in primary school _____

_____

_____

Pocket money _____ What he/she spent it on ____

Household chores _____

_____

Names of secondary schools _____

_____

Favourite subjects _____

_____

Favourite teachers _____

_____

Best friends in secondary school _____

_____

Favourite books _____

_____

Favourite music _____

_____

Favourite television shows, movies and actors

Favourite sports

Childhood holidays

Makes and models of family cars

Childhood pets

Special childhood memories

ATTACH A FAVOURITE PHOTOGRAPH FROM
YOUR PARTNER'S CHILDHOOD HERE

My Partner's Adult Years

Tertiary education _____

_____

Degrees and diplomas _____

_____

His/her first job was with _(name of organisation)_ _____

_____

Position held _____

Weekly salary _____ Price of a newspaper _____

Special friends _____

_____

_____

Favourite sporting teams _____

_____

Favourite music _____

_____

Favourite books _____

_____

Favourite television shows _____

_____

Favourite movies and actors _____

_____

> Growing old
> is mandatory;
> growing up is
> optional.
>
> _Chili Davis_

Other jobs *(names of organisations and positions held)*

_____
_____
_____
_____

Special interests and pastimes

_____
_____
_____
_____

Special memories and achievements

_____
_____
_____
_____
_____
_____

What he/she considers his/her strengths to be

_____
_____
_____
_____
_____
_____

How We Met

How we met
_____
_____
_____
_____

Our first date
_____
_____

What we liked about each other
_____
_____
_____
_____

We became engaged on (date)
_____

How we celebrated our engagement
_____
_____
_____

Description of the ring
_____
_____

Our song
_____
_____

We were engaged for (length of time)
_____

Special memories of our courtship
_____
_____
_____
_____

ATTACH A FAVOURITE PHOTOGRAPH
OF YOU AND YOUR PARTNER HERE

All I really, really want
our love to do is
to bring out the best
in me and in you too.

Joni Mitchell

Our Wedding

Date of marriage _____

Where it took place _____

Conducted by _____

The bride wore _____

_____

_____

The bridegroom wore _____

_____

Maid of honour and bridesmaids _____

_____

_____

Best man and groomsmen _____

_____

_____

Music played _____

Guests included _____

_____

_____

_____

My whole heart for my whole life.

French Saying

ATTACH A FAVOURITE PHOTOGRAPH
OF YOUR WEDDING HERE

Our Years Together

So far we have been together for _____ years

Our first home together _____

_____

Our family home _____

_____

Our closest friends _____

_____

_____

_____

What we did well together _____

_____

_____

_____

Our most prized possessions _____

_____

_____

_____

> Love is a promise,
> love is a souvenir,
> once given,
> never forgotten,
> never let it disappear.
>
> *John Lennon*

Our highs _____

_____

_____

_____

Our lows _____

_____

_____

_____

My Children

Full name _____

Date of birth _____ Time of birth _____

Birthplace _____

Colouring _____ Eye colour _____

Who he/she takes after _____

Personality and temperament _____

_____

_____

Full name _____

Date of birth _____ Time of birth _____

Birthplace _____

Colouring _____ Eye colour _____

Who he/she takes after _____

Personality and temperament _____

_____

_____

Full name _____

Date of birth _____ Time of birth _____

Birthplace _____

Colouring _____ Eye colour _____

Who he/she takes after _____

Personality and temperament _____

_____

_____

NOTE: IF YOU HAVE MORE CHILDREN, SIMPLY PHOTOCOPY THIS PAGE AND ADD IT TO THE BACK OF THE JOURNAL.

Special Thoughts
and Memories
About My Children

_____
_____
_____
_____
_____
_____
_____
_____
_____
_____
_____
_____
_____
_____
_____
_____
_____
_____
_____
_____

ATTACH A FAVOURITE PHOTOGRAPH OF
YOU AND YOUR CHILDREN HERE

A child can ask questions that
a wise man cannot answer.

Author Unknown

My Cousins

Children of my mother's siblings

_____

_____

_____

_____

_____

_____

_____

_____

_____

_____

Children of my father's siblings

_____

_____

_____

_____

_____

_____

_____

_____

_____

_____

My Partner's Cousins

Children of my partner's mother's siblings
_____
_____
_____
_____
_____
_____
_____
_____
_____
_____

Children of my partner's father's siblings
_____
_____
_____
_____
_____
_____
_____
_____
_____
_____
_____

Nieces and Nephews

My nieces and nephews

_____
_____
_____
_____
_____
_____
_____
_____
_____

My partner's nieces and nephews

_____
_____
_____
_____
_____
_____
_____
_____

World Events Remembered

HOW OLD AND WHERE I WAS WHEN…

John F. Kennedy was assassinated
_____

_____

Man landed on the moon
_____

_____

I purchased my first television
_____

_____

Elvis was found dead
_____

_____

John Lennon was assassinated
_____

_____

Prince Charles and Diana were married
_____

_____

The Space Shuttle Challenger exploded
_____

_____

The Berlin Wall fell
_____

_____

Princess Diana died in a car crash
_____

_____

Concord crashed in France
_____

_____

Terrorists attacked the World Trade Center and Pentagon
_____

_____

My Thoughts on Family to Share With You

> The great gift
> of family life is
> to be intimately
> acquainted
> with people you
> might never even
> introduce yourself
> to, had life not
> done it for you.
>
> *Kendall Hailey*